FLOWERS OF THE WOODS

FLOWERS
OF THE WOODS

By

E. J. SALISBURY
C.B.E., D.Sc., F.R.S.
Director, Royal Botanic Gardens, Kew

The KING PENGUIN *Books*
PUBLISHED BY PENGUIN BOOKS LIMITED
LONDON *and* NEW YORK
1946

THE KING PENGUIN BOOKS

Editor: N. B. L. Pevsner
Technical Editor: R. B. Fishenden

FIRST PUBLISHED 1946

MADE IN GREAT BRITAIN

Text Pages printed by
R. & R. CLARK, LTD., EDINBURGH
Set in Monotype Bembo

Colour Plates
Made and Printed by JOHN SWAIN & SON, LTD.

Cover design by
Rosemary and Clifford Ellis

PUBLISHED BY

PENGUIN BOOKS LTD.
HARMONDSWORTH MIDDLESEX
ENGLAND

PENGUIN BOOKS INC.
245 FIFTH AVENUE
NEW YORK

THE *Flora Londiniensis* from which the accompanying plates are reproduced was a magnificent folio work published from 1777 to 1791. It was issued in seventy-two numbers each containing illustrations and descriptions of six species. The earlier volumes of twelve numbers portrayed the plants that grew within a radius of ten miles round London in a series of 432 exquisite folio plates which were engraved on copper and coloured by hand, but the later volumes included some species from distant parts of Britain.

The author of the *Flora Londiniensis* was William Curtis, the son of a tanner of Alton in Hampshire, and it was due to one John Legg, an ostler at the Crown Inn, Alton, who had a considerable knowledge of wild plants, that William Curtis became enthused with a love of botany. He was born in 1746 and, like his father, belonged to the Society of Friends. He came to London as an apothecary and was in business at Gracechurch Street in 1772 when, at the age of twenty-six, he was appointed to succeed Alchorne as Botanical Demonstrator to the Apothecaries' Society at Chelsea. He resigned five years later and constructed a garden in Bermondsey where he cultivated many wild plants. It was at this time that he embarked on the *Flora Londiniensis* and, subsequently, on the more popular *Botanical Magazine*. The former was a financial failure, owing to the costly production which was not met by the £18 or £27 at which it was published, despite the much greater purchasing power of money then as compared with the present day. The *Botanical Magazine* was a financial success and, together with very substantial contributions from friends (Dr. Lettsom gave him £500), enabled Curtis to continue the *Flora* for a time.

In his preface to the first volume of the *Flora*, Curtis

expressed the intention to take the greatest pains to have the figures 'drawn from living specimens most expressive of the general habit or appearance of the plant as it grows wild, to place each plant, as much as is consistent, in the most pleasing point of view'. That he succeeded in a high degree in this ambition the majority of the plates bear witness, for they represent the most successful portrayals of British wild flowers that have ever been achieved.

Many of the illustrations in the first fasciculus were drawn and engraved by Kilburn, of whose work the Honeysuckle is an admirable example (Plate 1). In the second fasciculus the name of Sansom appears and most of the signed illustrations come from his hand till the fifth fasciculus, when on most of the plates there appears the name of James Sowerby, the first and ablest of a family of botanical artists. The last fasciculus contains illustrations by S. Edwards. A Mr. Milton also contributed drawings, and all the colouring was carried out by Mr. William Graves.

A second edition illustrated by 648 plates was published under the editorship of Sir William Hooker, consisting of a re-issue of the original work together with two additional volumes in 1821 and 1828 respectively. The first impressions of Curtis's original edition represent the high-water mark of botanical coloured illustration in England.

Perhaps one of the greatest charms of English woodlands is the never-ceasing change throughout the year. Each season has its own particular appeal, whether it be the bursting of the buds in springtime, the full canopy of the green mantle in summer, or, in winter, the nakedness of the tracery of bough and twig which reveals to us the beauty of constructional form and functional efficiency of the trees and shrubs.

Unlike the evergreen forests of the rainy tropics, where the humid warmth throughout the year encourages perpetual growth, the most characteristic type of woodland in our own clime sheds its foliage in the autumn, and this change from the full leafage of the summer months to the bare branches of winter enables the trees to withstand climatic rigours that could not be tolerated by large-leaved trees or shrubs that retained their foliage throughout the cold season.

The green leaves absorb a considerable part of the sunlight that falls upon them, and by means of this supply of energy they are enabled to combine the carbon dioxide of the air with the constituents of water taken up from the soil, to form sugars which are subsequently used either as a source of energy or as building material for the plant's body.

The more leaves that the tree or herb bears the more food it will be able to produce, and so when we go into a beechwood in summer the grateful shade helps us to realise how much of the sunshine is arrested by the canopy above and utilised by the tree's chemical machinery.

But the impression we have of a shady woodland is in fact very misleading because the interior seems much less shaded, in comparison with the open, than it actually is. Our mistaken judgment is because, directly we go into the shade, the pupils of our eyes dilate so that to a considerable extent we compensate automatically for the changes of light intensity that surround us. If, however, we use appropriate physical instruments, which do not of course automatically adjust themselves like our eyes, we find out the astonishing fact that the light intensity near the ground in a beechwood on a bright summer's day is often only about one-thirtieth of that in the open and rarely more than one-seventh. But under the lighter canopy of birch trees the intensity may be one-fifth or even as much as one-half that outside. If we were to make similar comparisons outside and inside these woods in the early springtime, before the leaves had formed, the proportion of the light beneath the branches would of course be far higher, and even in a beechwood might attain to two-fifths that in the open, whilst in a birch-wood in spring the light is often one-half or three-quarters that outside.

Since in summer so large a part of the rays that the plant uses for manufacturing its food are filtered out of the daylight by the leaves overhead, it is evident that there will not be a great deal left over that is useful for any plants of low growth that may occupy the ground.

We can scarcely be surprised therefore to find that most of the more characteristic woodland flowers are produced by plants whose natural mode of growth and development is such that, in one way or another, the difficulty of obtaining sufficient light is either evaded or minimised.

The shade problem may, for instance, be said to be evaded by the climbing plant, which through using other plants, such as the neighbouring shrubs, for support, can produce much longer stems than if its resources of material had to be expended on stems sufficiently robust to support themselves. By this means the shoots of the climbing plant are able to reach the light, especially near the edge of the woodland, and thus develop the leaves where they can effectively manufacture their food. It might then be said of such plants that they rely on the shoulders of their neighbours to hoist them up into the sunshine.

One of the most beautiful of such climbers is the common Honeysuckle (Plate 1) whose fragrant trusses of pale blossoms emit their odour, especially after dusk, and thus their presence is advertised to the moths by whose aid the pollen is transferred from stamen to stigma and the develop-ing ovules thereby caused to mature into fertile seeds.

The conspicuousness of the flowers to the insects' eyes in the dusk is greater than to ours, since some light rays which to our human eyes are invisible are perceived by the eyes of the moths. The name Honeysuckle refers picturesquely to the nectar which these long-tongued insects suck up and which we can see and taste if we slit up the tube of the flower on a warm damp evening. Shakespeare also uses the name Woodbine, and the appropriateness of this is sometimes seen where the Honeysuckle has twined its stems, in its usual anti-clockwise direction, around a supporting hazel wand. In a few years the hazel stem looks like a spiral baluster, its increasing girth bulging out between the constricting turns of the Woodbine's tough stems.

The beautiful representation from Curtis's *Flora Londiniensis* (Plate 1) portrays very faithfully the changing colour of the flowers from the bud stage to maturity. The unopened flowers are deeply tinged with crimson and, as they open, become paler and change within from white to yellow. After the flowers are shed the small green berries enlarge and eventually become bright red. The illustration shows only the usual shape of leaf which occurs on the flowering shoots, but if a bush be cut down, as when a hedge is laid or a woodland is coppiced, we often find leaves which, instead of being shaped like those of a privet, are lobed and slightly reminiscent of an oak leaf.

Only two other woody climbers commonly grow in our English woodlands. These are the Woody Nightshade (*Solanum dulcamara*; Plate 2), with flowers like miniature potato blooms, and the Wild Clematis or Virgin's Bower (*Clematis vitalba*; Plate 3) whose fragrant cream flowers are later replaced by the feathery fruits which give the shrub its autumn appellation of Old Man's Beard. The Woody Nightshade belongs to the same genus as the Potato and in both alike the flowers bear a cone of five triangular stamens from each of which the pollen escapes through a pair of rounded holes at their tips. The leaves when bruised have a peculiar and unpleasant odour and, if chewed, taste bitter at first and afterwards sweetish, from which fact derives its other name of Bitter-sweet. The poisonous properties of the plant, as also its former medicinal repute, are due to the presence of an alkaloid. The particular charm of the flowers is an outcome not merely of their form but of

9

the colour contrasts provided by the yellow stamens against the purple petals each with its pair of green spots near the base.

The Wild Clematis is our only English representative of the large genus Clematis, of which there are over two hundred species widely distributed as native plants, and most of them woody climbers which cling to their supports by the coiling of their leaf-stalks which, once attached, thicken and become woody. In tropical forests such woody climbers exhibit a great variety and profusion, attain to large dimensions and are called lianas. But if woody climbers are rare with us, our hedges, which in large part represent the artificial counterpart of the natural margin of the woods and the woodland margins themselves, are often bedecked with climbers which die down every season. Such, for instance, is the White Bryony, whose greenish blossoms, amidst leaves shaped like those of a vegetable marrow, can be seen festooned many feet above the ground. Its long shoots develop in spring from a very large root like an irregularly forked parsnip, filled with food material at the expense of which the extensive growth is made possible. It is this root which gave the plant its name of Wild Mandrake, and the herbalists of old, by appropriate trimming and embellishment, made the dried root resemble a shrunken human form and thus, as Thomas Lupton wrote at the end of the sixteenth century, 'the Counterfeat Mandrag which hath been sold by deceyuers for much money' was bought by the credulous and was no doubt as effective as its prototype.

The Black Bryony too is an interesting climber because it is the sole representative in these northern climes of a family that otherwise is exclusively found in tropical or warm temperate regions. The Yams are important economic members of this family, which are cultivated for their fleshy roots in tropical America, and it is noteworthy that the shining, heart-shaped leaves of the Black Bryony and the bunches of poisonous red berries have a distinctly exotic appearance draping an English hedgerow. The shoots, when they first develop in spring, look rather like long attenuated asparagus pushing up amidst the stems of the shrubs till they reach the light. This considerable growth is at the expense of the food stored up during the previous summer in the thick black root which gives the plant its appellation.

But more even than the White and Black Bryony, the festoons of Honeysuckle or of Old Man's Beard, the blue trusses of the Bush Vetch (Plate 4) or climbing Fumitory, we associate with our woodlands a type of plant which evades the shade problem in another way. Nothing is more characteristic of the English woodland than the springtime sheets of Primroses and Wild Hyacinths (*Scilla nutans*; Plate 6), of Wood Anemones and Lesser Celandines. There too we meet the Snowdrops of February and March and the Daffodils of April.

All of these alike have an underground storehouse of food, whether it be the swollen roots of the Lesser Celandine, the creeping underground fleshy stem of the Wood Anemone, or the bulbs of the Snowdrop and Daffodil. Such food stores, put by the previous season, enable these plants to produce their flowers and foliage early in the year, before the canopy of foliage of shrub and tree cuts off the light above. Indeed if we visit our woodlands later in the season, when clothed in their full mantle of verdure, the leaves of these herbs will probably be found to have already turned yellow if they have not already withered away. Here too, then, the shade problem is evaded through a precocious development rendered possible owing to a food store put by in the previous season.

True it is that we shall find some of the familiar woodland herbs retaining their foliage through most of the year. It is so for the Dog's Mercury (*Mercurialis perennis*; Plate 5). But this too forms its leaves early and most of its food is manufactured during the early months of the year when the shade is slight. Moreover, if we note where the sheets

of Dog's Mercury grow, we shall find that they corre-
spond to those parts where a considerable amount of light
filters through the trees in summer. The inconspicuous
green flowers of the Dog's Mercury are of two kinds,
each borne on different plants, so that a large patch may
only produce those containing the yellow stamens or those
that bear the female flowers and later fruits. Although
the flowers are small and green, the Dog's Mercury draws
our attention because it is one of the earliest plants to
clothe the ground, especially in the beechwoods, with a
carpet of bright green. It spreads very rapidly by means
of its underground stems, and when first the shoots
emerge above the soil they are bent, but straighten out
when exposed to the light. The bent form of emerging
shoot which we see in the Wood Anemone also means
that the leafy apex is drawn up through the soil and debris
of twigs and leaves instead of pushing its way upwards,
and by this mode of growth resistance is diminished. The
leaves of the Wood Sorrel (Plate 12) and the 'Town
Hall Clock' (Plate 13) are bent in a similar manner and
also show the same straightening after reaching the
light. The shoots of the Wild Arum, on the other hand,
push upwards like spears and so do the leaves of the Wild
Daffodil.

Two of the earliest flowers to greet our eyes in spring
are the Primrose and Wood Anemone. The name Primrose (*Primula acaulis*) actually implies the first flower, and
Lyte in his *Herbal* of 1554 spells the name Primerose, to
which it has some claim since flowers can sometimes be
found in sheltered places even in January. One of its less
familiar popular names is Spring-flower. The illustration
from Curtis's *Flora* (Plate 7) shows clearly the characteristic corrugated leaves, and, on the left-hand side, the
manner in which the edges of the young leaves are rolled
backwards. There are two kinds of Primrose plants, and
the one which is figured is that called 'thrum-eyed', in
which the five stamens are situated near the top of the

flower-tube. Half-way down the tube of such a flower is situated the globular stigma, at the end of a short stalk arising from the top of the young fruit.

In the other type of flower the stigma has a longer stalk and is in consequence situated at the mouth of the flower-tube, whilst the five stamens form a ring about half-way down the tube and so are not visible except when we split the flower-tube longitudinally; but the stigma is easily seen at the top of the tube, like a greenish pin's head, hence the name 'pin-eyed' for this type. Seed is only readily set when the stigmas of thrum-eyed flowers receive pollen from pin-eyed flowers or when the stigmas of pin-eyed flowers receive pollen from thrum-eyed flowers. Such cross-pollination is clearly facilitated by the fact that the stamens of the one type occupy the same height in the tube as the stigma in the other; so when an insect seeking honey passes its 'tongue' down the tube, the pollen adheres at the appropriate levels to bring about the most effective pollination. The pollen grains, thus transferred, grow and effect fertilisation so that the ovules are converted into seeds. When ripe these become liberated by the splitting-open of the top of the capsule into teeth. When the air is dry these teeth spread apart, but when the air is humid the outer side of the teeth expands more than the inner and so the teeth close together and the seeds remain shut in, only to escape under those conditions favourable for their dispersal.

The Wood Anemone or Wind Flower (*Anemone nemorosa*, Plate 8) normally comes into bloom about the first day in April, but it is usually not till the month is well advanced that the woodlands show white drifts of the blossoms. If we visit an Anemone wood on a bright day, we shall see the flowers open like six-rayed, or five-rayed, stars to the sunshine. But if we were to visit the same wood on a cold wet day, or after dusk, we should find these same flowers with their heads drooping and the white segments no longer spread apart, but closed together. This feature has not escaped the countryman's notice and is picturesquely enshrined in the popular name of Granny's Nightcap. The flowers contain a large number of stamens, actually about sixty, though some flowers contain over ninety, each producing a considerable number of pollen grains. Compared with many flowers this profusion of pollen might appear remarkable, but actually the flowers secrete no nectar but are visited by bees and flies for the sake of the pollen which they collect, and if such pollen flowers did not produce more pollen than flowers which are visited for nectar there might well be no surplus to ensure the survival of the species. The illustration shows the underground stem, situated a short distance below the surface, from which the leaves and flowering shoots develop, and which is stored with food during the late spring and early summer to serve for the early growth of the new leaves the following year.

With the Wood Anemones we associate the Lesser Celandine (*Ficaria verna*; Plate 9) whose starry yellow blooms stand out against the background of shiny heart-shaped leaves. Here too the early growth is provided by a store of food contained in a bunch of swollen roots attached to a little spike-like bud that pushes through to the surface in January and expands to form a rosette of leaves from amongst which the flowers develop in February and March. Here too the sunny day brings about an opening of the flowers so that the woodland clearing is bespangled with these golden stars, but night-time or a wet day finds them with the, usually eight, petals closed together, showing only their dull-greenish undersides and the three green sepals which envelop them. At the base of each of the petals is a tiny scale beneath which the nectar is secreted which attracts the visiting insects. Note also, although the flowers are visited mainly for the nectar, there are a number of stamens, most commonly twenty-one but sometimes as many as sixty-three, which warns us that, though a flower visited for pollen alone is unlikely to succeed unless it has a moderately large output of pollen, economy in pollen production is not necessarily exhibited by all flowers visited by insects. Indeed all members of the Buttercup family, to which the Lesser Celandine and Wood Anemone belong, are rather lavish in this respect, even such specialised flowers as the Aconite which are visited only by bumble-bees.

Actually there are two kinds of Lesser Celandine—one of which sets seed freely; the other rarely fruits, but reproduces freely by bulbils, which are produced between the stem and the base of the leaf just where the shoot normally arises. These modified shoots, which really consist of a very small bud with a large swollen root attached, readily drop off, and when they have fallen to the ground become spread about by rainwater and give rise to new plants the following spring.

Our illustration shows two kinds of roots on a flowering specimen, namely, the branched feeding roots, which are slender and sometimes several inches in length, and the swollen storage roots. Of these latter, some which were formed the previous year, have already become somewhat shrivelled as almost all the food stores they contained were used up when the leaves and flowers were formed. Other storage roots are smooth and swollen and represent the provision for the following spring.

Far larger food stores are provided by the Wild Arum (*Arum maculatum*; Plate 10), the spear-like shoots of which arise from a solid, underground stumpy stem copiously provided with starch. This corm, as it is called, is well shown in our illustration, and though the plant is a poisonous one, heat appears to render the corm innocuous, and dried and powdered it was formerly employed as food, being sold as 'Portland Sage', and the name 'starch-root' is another tribute to the same use. The popular names under which this plant has been known are very varied and are mostly associated with its diversity of characteristic features. What is commonly called the 'flower' is in reality, like the 'flower' of the cultivated

Arum, a stem bearing a number of flowers surrounded by a single protective sheath. The flower-bearing axis is shown removed from the enveloping sheath on the right-hand side of the illustration. It consists of a swollen purple apex below which are a number of sterile male flowers taking the form of a girdle of downwardly-pointing hairs. Below these is another girdle of flowers producing pollen only, and still lower a girdle of female flowers which bear no stamens but only produce fruits. Flies are attracted by the rather putrid smell of the purple apex, the colour of which is not unlike that of decomposing flesh and from which the country name of 'Dead-men's Fingers' is derived.

The flies crawl past the hairs, which are situated just beneath the narrowest part of the tubular region of the sheath, but since these hairs will bend freely downwards and in the upward direction touch the sheath, the flies are trapped till the hairs wither. In the flask-like base of the sheath the flies become copiously dusted with the pollen shed from the girdle of male flowers, and this pollen they transfer to the female flowers as they crawl upwards.

The dark structure appearing above the tubular part of the sheath suggested to our forefathers the dark-gowned parson's figure of a former age above the pulpit's edge, and hence the appellation 'Jack-in-the-pulpit'. The familiar designation 'Cuckoo-pint' refers to the belief that cuckoos drank the liquid that collected in the base of the sheath. The name Arrowroot clearly derives from the arrowhead-like leaves, and the use of this same name for the imported product may well have been an instance of name transference rather than, as has been stated, an erroneous belief in the efficacy of Arrowroot against poisoned arrows.

When autumn sees the flower-spike replaced by the bright scarlet berries, the local name of Wake Robin, which we might very freely paraphrase the Red Resurrection, emphasises for us how these vivid autumn fruits emerge from the withered miserable-looking structure of the summer months, whilst the name of Poison-berry reminds

16

us that children have died from eating them, owing to the presence of an irritant, saponin.

Even more tolerant of the shade than the Cuckoo-pint is the Wood Sorrel (*Oxalis acetosella*; Plate 12), so called because the leaves if chewed have a similar acid flavour to the Sorrel of the meadow. The dainty flowers are usually white veined with purple, though less commonly purple throughout. The leaves rather resemble those of a Clover, and like the latter they consist of three leaflets which close together at night. But whereas in the Clover the leaflets move upwards together at night, those of the Wood Sorrel close together downwards, a movement which also takes place if the leaves are exposed to bright sunlight and which is brought about by loss of moisture from the slightly swollen attachments of the leaflets to the main stalk. In addition to the normal flowers produced early in the season there are others which do not open and have no petals. Both kinds can form fruits, but the more conspicuous flowers produce fruits that contain more seeds. The stalk bearing the young fruit bends downwards, but again becomes erect as the seeds approach maturity. The ripe capsule ruptures at a touch and the contents are violently shot out, owing to an elastic whitish covering which envelops each seed. The store of food which here provides for the spring development is found not in the stem but in the leaf-bases, which persist as little swollen structures after the leaves and leaf-stalks have been shed. Birds sometimes feed on these leaf-bases, from which fact derives the popular name of 'Bird's Bread-and-cheese'. Other names, such as 'Cuckoo's Victuals' and 'Hare's Meat' are probably tributes to the edible nature of these food reserves rather than evidence that they are eaten by the particular animals designated.

The 'Town Hall Clock' or Moschatel (*Adoxa moschatellina*; Plate 13) similarly stores its surplus food in swollen scale-like structures, the underground stems being, here too, slender and serving mainly to spread apart the

B

buds which form the flowering shoots of the next season. The flowering stems of the 'Town Hall Clock' bear five flowers and, as the illustration clearly shows, they form a rectangular head in which each of the four sides is occupied by a single green flower suggestive of faces of a clock tower. Like many woodland plants it is a shy fruiter, but under favourable conditions the flowers are succeeded by a group of fleshy-green berries. Normally the plant of one year is replaced by others produced at the ends of the horizontal underground shoots, the connections decaying away at an early stage.

It will be realised that the 'Town Hall Clock' can be regarded as really an annual plant in which persistence from year to year depends mainly on annually-produced buds instead of, as with most annuals, on renewal by seedlings. It is this annual habit that explains why it is that we sometimes find the 'Town Hall Clock' in profusion whilst if we visit the same wood the following year the number of plants may be quite few. The flowers are visited by small insects attracted by the musk-like scent and the nectar which is freely exposed. In this way pollination may be effected, and as the stigma becomes receptive before the pollen is shed, the chances are in favour of cross-pollination. But although the stamens at first stand away from the stigma, they afterwards bend inwards so that, if the stigma is still receptive, self-pollination may take place. In the event of fertile seed being produced, its subsequent germination would appear, from experiments, to be favoured by having been subjected to severe frost.

A feature one cannot fail to notice during a woodland stroll in late spring is the number of characteristic woodland plants which are social in habit. Several of those we have mentioned, such as Wood Anemones, Dog's Mercury, Wild Hyacinths and Lesser Celandines, often form extensive drifts in which the one kind of plant predominates almost to the exclusion of others. This feature is mainly an outcome of the fact that most woodland plants depend more on vegetative spread than on reproduction from seed. The seeds of woodland plants, compared with those of non-woodland species, are usually large, sometimes conspicuously so, and thus provide a larger food supply for the germinating seedling. But even so the new shoot, formed at the end of the horizontal underground stems of the Anemone or Dog's Mercury, from a daughter bulb of the Wild Hyacinth or a bulbil of the Lesser Celandine, is obviously better provided with food and better able to grow up into the light than a seedling. Usually it is only in certain favourable seasons that we find any profusion of seedling Hyacinths or Wood Anemones, and those of the Dog's Mercury are invariably sparse. The vegetative mode of spread has two main advantages: the one just mentioned, that spread can proceed with greater tolerance of shaded conditions, and the second, that the continuous occupation of the ground by one kind of plant results in a uniformity of growth that not only produces mutual shelter but tends to exclude other competing species or at least to retard their aggressive development. Any bare ground in a woodland tends to become occupied sooner or later by some plant or other, and if the neighbour of one plant is about the same height as itself, conditions are more favourable than if that neighbour be of another, potentially taller kind, that will cut off some of the sunlight.

By the time that the shrubs and trees are in full leaf we shall find the leaves of the Hyacinths and Anemones are beginning to turn yellow, and a little later they have withered away. The leaves do their work between the time they develop in the spring and the shade of summer. But there are others, like the Woodruff, which are green all the year round and so can manufacture their food whenever the air around is sufficiently warm for the chemical processes of food formation to go on, provided the shade is not too dense. Actually the Wood Sorrel is also practically evergreen and forms its new leaves before the cold winter puts a check to growth. Such plants do not therefore waste some of the precious time in spring, when the shade in the woods is still slight, in forming new leaves, and so it is scarcely surprising that they can often grow in shadier situations than the vernal species.

The Woodruff is so called because the leafy whorls which beset the stem at intervals suggested to our forefathers the ruffs of Elizabethan days. If we gather some of the plant and allow it to dry we shall find it is scented like new-mown hay. The reason is that, like the Vernal Grass which gives hay its characteristic perfume, the Woodruff contains the substance coumarin. This accounts for its name of Sweet-grass and for its use in flavouring beer, whence a local name for the plant of Mugwort, a name more commonly used for an Artemisia that was employed in the same manner.

Although it is the spring flowers which we more particularly associate with the woods, they, perhaps more than any type of wild countryside, show a marked succession of changes as one season of the year gives place to another. The Snowdrops, Daffodils and Lesser Celandines of the early spring give place to the Anemones, Wild Hyacinths, Wild Garlic, and these in turn to the Foxgloves, the Mulleins and Golden Rods. And as we follow this procession of the floral seasons we note that, as we might well have anticipated, it is the dwellers in the shadier parts that usually flower first, and as the year advances we must look for the woodland flowers nearer the edges, along the borders of the sylvan glades or in the clearings. In the height of summer we shall commonly find the ground in the shadier parts of the beechwoods and oakwoods almost devoid of any flowers, perhaps even of foliage, from which we might wonder whether the soil itself were infertile were it not that this same soil is soon clothed with a wealth of vegetation, when the light is let in by the felling of a tree or the coppicing of the undergrowth.

Nothing perhaps is more beautiful than the wealth and

variety of the plant covering which often appears in the second season following the coppicing of a damp oakwood. Here plants, which previously we had seen as scattered and perhaps infrequent denizens of the woodland margin, are now seen in profusion. Sheets of Foxgloves and Rosebay Willow-herb spread a purple mantle over the erstwhile bare soil, relieved here and there by the stately columns of the yellow Mullein or bright patches of Golden Rod. Here also flourish the prickly-headed Teazels and sheets of the dainty Cow-wheat. When lit by the rays of the sun, the tall Marsh Thistles vie with the Teazels in attracting the attention of the handsome silver-washed Fritillary butterflies, the Red Admirals, Peacocks and freshly-emerged Brimstones.

If we had visited this same area during the winter we should have seen many of these plants of the clearings as rosettes of leaves. The Teazel rosettes consist of leaves close-pressed to the soil, each beset with bristle-like hairs on swollen bases, while the rosettes of the Mullein appear clothed in their flannel covering of richly-branched hairs the collection of which, as a penance, to serve for the wicks of altar lights, gave rise to the name of Candle-wick. Rosette plants are practically unknown amongst the real shade flora of the woodland but constitute an appreciable part of the more characteristic species of the clearings and margins of the woods. There grow also the pretty Pink Campions, the blue spires of the Bugles and the yellow of the Weasel-snout (*Galeobdolon luteum*; Plate 14). These members of the Deadnettle tribe, like another member of the same family, the Ground Ivy, are often to be found freely in the partial shade of the uncut woodland, but in a non-flowering state. This is also true of many other woodland plants, such as the Pig-nut: they only flower well when they are growing in good light.

The Mullein, which most commonly grows in these situations, is known botanically as *Verbascum thapsus* and bears good witness to the utility of Latin names, for in

England alone it is known by between forty and fifty popular names, and when we remember that it shares a similar wealth of aliases in other European countries the need for some designation common to all is obvious. The English names fall into groups according to some appearance or property, supposed or real. The very hairy leaves are responsible for: Feltwort, Duffle, Fluffweed, Adam's Flannel, Blanket Leaf, and Mullein itself, which is spelt Mulleyne by Lyte and according to both Lyte and Gerard is a modified form of Welleyne. The tall spike of yellow flowers has given origin to the names of Hedge Torch, Ag-taper (*i.e.* Hedge Taper), Golden Rod, whilst its reputed value as a remedy for chest complaints gave rise to names such as Lungwort.

The irregular manner in which the golden-yellow flowers appear on the inflorescence is due to the fact that it is not a simple structure like the Foxglove with the oldest flowers at the base and the youngest at the tip. The cylindrical flower-head is really a succession of bunches of flowers each consisting of a number of flowers of differing ages, some of which may be in bud whilst others may have already formed fruits.

The Teazel (*Dipsacus sylvestris*; Plate 11) owes part of its charm to the peculiar sequence of development of its flowers which begin to open as a girdle of blooms half-way up the conical flower-head. As these wither, flowers open above and below, so that at a later stage we see two girdles of bloom which separate more and more till the wave of blossoms has reached the opposite ends. To understand how this comes about you should look at a Water Forget-me-not where you will see that the flowering shoot bears a central flower, which opens first, and this is followed by the flowers borne on the two branches on either side in sequence from the base to the tips. If we imagine a number of inflorescences of Forget-me-not, with the two arms in a vertical plane, arranged like the spokes of a wheel, the order of flowering would be just such as we see in the Teazel, and it is in fact a complex inflorescence of that character. The well-known use of Teazel heads to raise the nap on cloth involved the use of a variety known as the Fuller's Teazel, in which the spiny structures of the head are bent backwards instead of being straight as in the common Teazel of our woodlands. The heads were attached to revolving cylinders, and the extent to which they were used is indicated by the fact that it is on record that in 1859 more than eighteen million heads were imported into this country from France by the cloth trade, all of which was additional to the home-grown supply.

Apart from the characteristic heads, the Teazel is also distinguished by the peculiar leaves, the pairs of which join together at the base to form cup-like receptacles in which water collects. Insects often get drowned in the liquid; other aquatic animals may live there in a sort of miniature aquarium, whence the popular name of Venus Bath. But it is very doubtful whether the plant obtains any appreciable benefit from the liquid, although it has been suggested that in a sense the Teazel may be an insectivorous plant in that the nitrogenous substances liberated during the decay of the dead insects may perhaps be partially absorbed by the leaves.

Another kind of Teazel, with much smaller, rather rounded heads and whitish flowers, also occurs in woodland clearings, but is much more local. It is known as the Shepherd's Rod, and, like its relative, dies after flowering, just as do the Mulleins. Foxgloves, too, often die after their first flowering, but quite commonly flower a second or sometimes even a third year, which brings home to us that each kind of plant has its normal span of life; although so far as the longer-lived perennials are concerned, we scarcely recognise the fact, because by the time that they die we have forgotten, if we ever knew, when their life began.

The flowers of the woodland clearings which form such

gardens in early summer, vary with the nature of the soil as do the woodlands themselves. On the heavier clays, especially those which contain lime, we may expect to find along the wood margin and by the rides that very handsome grass the Hairy Brome (*Bromus asper*; Plate 15), often growing six or seven feet high and easily distinguished by its graceful drooping heads and the downwardly-directed hairs which clothe the stems. The broad leaves are hairy too and when covered with hoar frost are even beautiful when dead. Here too in spring we may find the spikes of the Early Purple Orchis (*Orchis mascula*; Plate 16) arising from the centre of a rosette of spotted leaves. The blooms contain no stamens like those of most flowers, but the pollen is produced in two masses situated on either side of the entrance to the spur. Each is located in a delicate pocket and bears a stalk with a sticky exposed end. If we use the pointed end of a pencil to simulate the head and tongue of an insect and push it into the spur of the flower, we shall find that the two masses of pollen adhere to it and come away from the pockets when we remove the pencil. In a few seconds the stalks bend and on the actual insect's head assume a position such that when another flower is visited the pollen adheres to the sticky stigma.

It is in the clayey woods too that the Herb Robert (*Geranium robertianum*; Plate 17) is a common feature of the clearings. Its scented foliage, rather aromatic but with a fusty, pungent tang, renders it agreeable to some and unpleasant to others. But whether we like its scent or not, the bright-green leaves against its crimson stems and the delicately-pencilled pink petals provide a colour scheme that all must admire.

The fruit consists of five swollen portions each containing a single seed surmounted by a beak-like structure. This latter at maturity consists of a central tapering column surrounded by five strips of tissue each attached to a seed-chamber. These strips suddenly contract and throw off the seed chambers and their contained seeds, it may be to a distance of as much as twenty feet from the parent plant. The seeds germinate in the spring or summer of the following year, so that the Herb Robert is often most abundant in woodland clearings during the second and third years after the undergrowth has been coppiced; subsequently the increased shade, due to the growth of the stool shoots, renders the conditions less and less favourable for such annual plants and the perennial shade flora takes their place, so that the Herb Robert is soon to be found only by the tracks and at the woodland margins.

In the dull days of late March and early April the blue stars of the Lesser Periwinkle (*Vinca minor*; Plate 18) are sometimes to be found in the clayey oakwoods, but they are much more familiar to us in gardens. The plant seldom fruits, but as the prostrate shoots root readily the absence of seeds is little of a handicap, whilst the evergreen foliage ensures that whenever the air is warm enough full use will be made of all the sunshine that reaches it. Still earlier in similar types of woodland we may be lucky enough to find the Green Hellebore (*Helleborus viridis*; Plate 19), the flowers of which are like green Christmas Roses. Each bloom is a green cup of five sepals followed by a ring of drinking horns, partly filled with nectar that attracts the visiting insects, which are in reality curiously-shaped petals. In the centre are numerous yellow stamens around the immature fruit.

On the lighter loams and sandy soils, especially those poor in lime, we may expect to see the clearings gay with Foxgloves and Golden Rod, and very possibly that charming trailer the Yellow Pimpernel (*Lysimachia nemorum*; Plate 20) which in Gerard's time grew between Highgate and Hampstead and was doubtless collected there by herbalists for its supposed 'power to mitigate pain'.

The Yellow Pimpernel belongs to a different genus, of the Primrose family, to the Scarlet Pimpernel although the two plants superficially resemble one another rather closely.

Both are prostrate in habit with similar leaves and with flowers that appear singly in the angle between leaf and stem, subsequently to be replaced by almost spherical capsules. But whereas in the Scarlet Pimpernel the top of the capsule comes off like a lid by a transverse split, liberating the seeds when ripe, in the Yellow Pimpernel the capsule wall splits into five teeth. The nearest relative is the Creeping Jenny, and like that plant the Yellow Pimpernel grows best in damp conditions but flowers best in full sun, so that it is in the recently coppiced areas that we should look for the profusion of its flowers in summer and its ripe fruits in autumn.

Of all the herbs which are to be met with on these lighter types of soil the Tutsan (*Hypericum androsaemum*; Plate 21), which usually grows singly here and there at the wood margin, had in Saxon times the greatest reputation for healing virtues. The English is in fact a corruption of '*tout sain*', meaning 'all heal'. Although the yellow flowers of this undershrub are rather inconspicuous, the berry-like black capsules and the beautifully-veined foliage give it a remarkably attractive appearance. If the leaves are crushed they emit a fragrant odour akin to that of other St. John's Worts. Perhaps its high repute was not entirely divorced from its comparatively innocuous character. In contrast we may recall that the Deadly Nightshade or Dwale (*Atropa belladonna*; Plate 22) is also a plant of the margin of woods, usually beechwoods on chalk soils. It is the source of atropine and its glossy black berries are highly poisonous, and children have been killed through eating them. It is even laid to its charge that wild rabbits which have fed freely upon the young shoots are poisonous after being cooked. To quote from Gerarde's *Herbal* of 1636: 'if you will follow my counsell, deale not with the same in any case and banish it from your garden and the use of it also, being a plant so furious and deadly'.

It is in the clearings of the beechwoods on the chalk hills that we commonly see the great sheets of Rosebay

Willow-herb (*Epilobium angustifolium*; Plate 23), like a crimson carpet, that almost suppresses every other plant about. Later, these flowers give place to long pods filled with a multitude of small seeds, attached to each of which is a parachute of silky hairs. When the pods ripen and burst open, the air soon becomes filled with the fluffy white seeds, like a summer snowstorm. But the rampant success of the plant is largely due to its rapid spread by the shoots which arise from the underground parts and which are clearly shown in the illustration. Extension at the rate of over a yard in a season is not unusual, so that one cannot be surprised that the plant soon occupies these clearings, burnt areas, or the bombed sites in London to the exclusion of almost any other plant. So beware of it even for the wild garden. In the damper woodland margins Soapwort (Plate 24) occasionally spreads in a similar way.

British woodlands are of many different kinds, each usually associated with a particular soil or situation and normally with one kind of tree much commoner than the others. On the heavy and more fertile soils of the South and Midlands the Common Oak is the prevailing tree, whilst in Yorkshire and the West Country, in the Lake District and in Wales, there are large stretches of oakwood (specially on the less fertile soils and hill slopes) where the Durmast Oak is prevalent, a tree distinguished from the Common Oak by the tapering base of the leaves, which have longer stalks and branched hairs on the underside, especially in the forks of the veins. The acorns of the Durmast Oak usually are without obvious stalks, whilst in the Common Oak, where the leaves have the shorter stalks, the acorns have long ones.

On calcareous soils the prevailing tree is usually the Beech, though sometimes the Ash, and these two kinds of woodland show a striking contrast in that, during the summer months in particular, the beechwood is deeply shaded whilst the interior of the ashwood is comparatively light. In the former the summer vegetation is often sparse or absent, whilst in the latter it may be abundant. Whereas we can walk through most Cotswold beechwoods or the beechwoods of the South Downs with comparative ease, owing to the absence of undergrowth, our progress in a Mendip ashwood may be seriously impeded by the dense thicket of shrubs, though the scrub-like margins of both are very similar as to density as well as the variety of the shrubs of which it is made up.

Birchwoods, from the considerable exposure that the Birch tree can endure, find a natural home above the limit of the oakwoods on our mountains, though early man has left but little of these easily felled forests except in Scotland. The free dispersal of the wind-borne fruits of the Birch and its tolerance for poor soils, whether dry or wet, has made the Birch tree one of the chief colonisers of felled woodland areas, especially on sandy or other soils poorly supplied with lime and other plant nutrients. In such situations birchwoods are commonly encountered, as, for instance, on the sandy commons of Surrey or the felled areas of Epping Forest. On similar soils the Scots Pine may play a like role, as we see on the sandy heaths of Surrey and Devonshire. Original woodlands of our native strain of Scots Pine are, however, only to be found to-day in Scotland itself, as for example in the beautiful forest of Rothiemurchus in Perthshire.

On calcareous soils the Ash tree may play the part of a coloniser, since its wind-borne fruits, the so-called keys, are freely dispersed, and provided the soils are well supplied with plant nutrients, the Ash tree can flourish in situations that are either dry or wet.

Even waterlogged soils may support woodland, but in such situations the trees are usually Birches and Willows, if the soils are of an acid type, whilst the fresher soils support woods of Alder. It is particularly in the alder-woods by the mountain streams of Wales that we see the golden Saxifrage in spring and the Welsh Poppies in summer. In the damp ashwoods of Kent we look for the sheets of Lady's Smock in April, whilst the wet flushes of the Mendip woodlands are gay in autumn with the Meadow Saffron. In the woods of the Common Oak we anticipate finding the carpets of Anemones and Celandines in spring, the regiments of Mulleins in summer and the best blackberries in autumn. Woods of Durmast Oak provide the favourable situation for Foxgloves and Golden Rod and for whortleberries. Each kind of woodland has its own features, sometimes expressed by the presence of kinds of plants that we do not find in every other type, sometimes by the greater profusion of those that may occur in almost all.

The woodland is, in fact, just as much a social assemblage as a community of human beings. It presents a great diversity of conditions, from the sunny margin and the woodland glade to the shaded interior, where little may grow but the autumnal Toadstools which, because they live on the decaying organic matter in the forest floor, are independent of the need for light which limits so many other plants. The trees, because of their height, determine the degree of shading to which the shrubs are subjected, and both together are responsible for the shade and shelter which the herbs covering the ground have imposed upon them. There are thus degrees of light and shade, of shelter and exposure, and the degree to which the diversity of these conditions promotes or restricts the growth of one or another kind of plant determines the niches which each species occupies. When the undergrowth is cut or trees are felled, or gaps are produced by natural causes, such as the ravages of gales or lightning, another set of conditions is established, and a sequence of changes ensues which tends ultimately to restore the original conditions till the rate of change is checked, because the most aggressive types suited to the conditions have become established. We might think that, when the tallest plants that can grow in a particular situation and cast an effective shade, had grown to maturity, change would practically cease. Actually this is not so, since no plants are immortal and the gaps caused by death initiate change, and since, which is still more important, even the longest-lived plants are gradually altering the conditions in which they live, if only by the debris of their own rejectamenta. The selective felling that we see carried out in some beechwoods gives us the illusion of stability, because this method of treatment is something in the nature of a continual rejuvenation. But examination of any old uncared-for woodland will lead us to realise that even under natural conditions the most stable-seeming vegetation undergoes change and that the communities of plants and animals, which we call wild life and which add so much to our enjoyment of the countryside, are not the perpetuation of events that have been achieved but of processes still continuing before our eyes, sometimes so slowly that we are unconscious of their occurrence; at other times—for instance when a wood is coppiced and again grows up—so rapid that we cannot fail to apprehend the marginal invasion and the subsequent retreat.

SELECTED LITERATURE FOR FURTHER READING

(i) *Biological*

Christy, Miller (1922), 'Primula Elatior; Its Distribution in Britain', *Journal of Ecology*, X, pp. 200-210.

Lundegardh, H. (1931), 'Environment and Plant Development' (English Trans.). Ed. Arnold, London.

Mukerji, S. K. (1936), 'Contributions to the Autocology of *Mercurialis perennis*', *Journal of Ecology*, XXIV, pp. 38-81, 317-339.

Salisbury, E. J. (1916), 'The Emergence of the Aerial Organs in Woodland Plants', *Journal of Ecology*, vol. iv, pp. 121-128.

(1921), 'Phenology and Habitat with special reference to the Phenology of Woodlands', *Quart. Jour. Royal Meteorological Society*, 47, pp. 252-263.

(1922), 'Stratification and Hydrogen-ion Concentration of the Soil in relation to Leaching and Plant Succession, with special reference to Woodlands', *Journal of Ecology*, IX, pp. 220-240.

(1924), 'The Effects of Coppicing as illustrated by the Woods of Hertfordshire', *Transactions Hertfordshire Nat. Hist. Soc.*, XVIII, pp. 1-21.

(1925), 'The Structure of Woodlands', *Festschrift Carl Schroter*, pp. 334-354. Zurich.

(1935), 'The Light Climate of Woodlands, *Berichte d. Schweizerischen Botanischen Gesellschaft*, pp. 1-11. Zurich.

(1942), *The Reproductive Capacity of Plants*. Bell & Sons, London.

Watt, A. S. (1923), 'Causes of Failure in Regeneration of British Oakwoods', *Journal of Ecology*, XI, pp. 1-48.

(1923), 'Causes of Failure in Regeneration of Beech', *Journal of Ecology*, XI, pp. 1-48.

(ii) *Regional*

Adamson, R. S. (1912), 'An Ecological Study of a Cambridgeshire Woodland', *Jour. Linn. Soc. Bot.* 40, pp. 339-387.

(1922), 'The Woodlands of Ditchen Park, Hampshire', *Journal of Ecology*, IX, pp. 114-219.

Baker, L. (1915), 'The Macclesfield District Vegetation', *Geographical Journal*, pp. 213-303.

Christy, Miller, and Worth, R. H. (1922), 'The Ancient Dwarfed Oak Woods of Dartmoor', *Trans. Devon Association*, 54, pp. 291-342.

Frazer, G. R. (1942), 'Notes on the Forest History of the Highlands', *Scots Mountaineering Club Journal*, pp. 1-20.

Henry, Augustine (1914), 'Woods and Trees of Ireland', *Louth Archaeological Journal*, pp. 1-9.

Moss, C. E. (1907), 'Geographical Distribution of the Vegetation of Somerset', *Roy. Geographical Soc. Journal.*

(1913), *The Vegetation of the Peak District.* Cambridge.

Salisbury, E. J. (1916), 'The Oak-Hornbeam Woods of Hertfordshire': Parts I-II, *Journal of Ecology*, IV, pp. 83-117. Parts III-IV, *ibid*. VI, pp. 14-52 (1918).

Salisbury, E. J., and Tansley, A. G. (1921), 'The Durmast Oakwoods of the Silurian and Malvernian Strata near Malvern', *Journal of Ecology*, IX, pp. 19-38.

Salisbury, E. J. (1925), 'The Vegetation of the Forest of Wyre', *Journal of Ecology*, XIII, pp. 314-321.

Smith, W. G., and Moss, C. E. (1903), 'Geographical Distribution of Vegetation in Yorkshire', *Geographical Journal*, pp. 1-27.

Smith, W. G., and Rankin, W. M. (1903), 'Vegetation of Yorkshire, Harrogate and Skipton District', *Geographical Journal*, pp. 1-30.

Tansley, A. G. (1939), 'The British Isles and their Vegetation', pp. 241-484. Cambridge.

Watt, A. S. (1923), 'Beech Communities on the Sussex Downs', *Journal of Ecology*, XII, pp. 145-204 and XIII, pp. 27-73, 1925.

(1926), 'Yew Communities of the South Downs', *Journal of Ecology*, XIV, pp. 282-316.

Watt, A. S., and Tansley, A. G. (1932), 'British Beechwoods' in Rubel's *Die Buchenwälder Europas*. Bern.

Wilson, M. (1911), 'Plant Distribution in the Woods of N.E. Kent', *Annals of Botany* 25, pp. 857-902.

Woodhead, T. W. (1906), 'The Ecology of Woodland Plants in the Neighbourhood of Huddersfield', *Jour. Linn. Soc. Bot.* 37, pp. 333-406.

Honeysuckle (Lonicera periclymenum)   *scale 2/5*

Woody Nightshade (Solanum dulcamara)   *scale* 1/3

Old Man's Beard (*Clematis vitalba*)   *scale 2/5*

Bush Vetch (Vicia Cracca)   *scale 2/5*

Dog's Mercury (Mercurialis perennis)   *scale 2/5*

Wild Hyacinth (Scilla nutans)   *scale* 1/3

Primrose (Primula acaulis)   *scale 2/3*

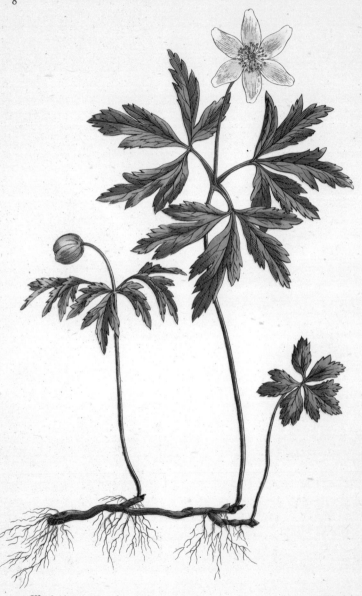

Wood Anemone (*Anemone nemorosa*) scale 2/3

Lesser Celandine (Ficaria verna)　　　　　*scale 2/3*

Wild Arum or Cuckoo-pint (Arum maculatum)   *scale 2/5*

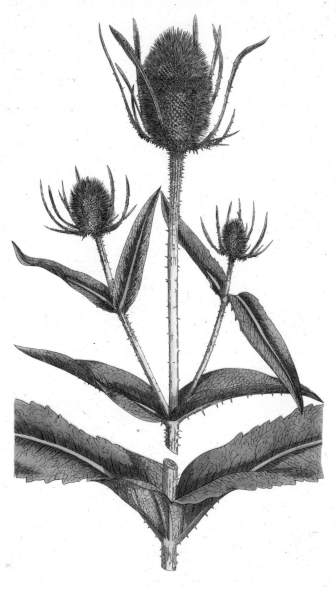

Teazel (Dipsacus sylvestris)　　　　　*scale 2/5*

Wood Sorrel (Oxalis acetosella)　　　　　*scale 2/3*

Town Hall Clock (Adoxa moschatellina)   *scale* 1/1

Weasel Snout or Yellow Deadnettle (Galeobdolon luteum) scale 2/5

Hairy Brome (Bromus asper)   *scale 2/5*

Early Purple Orchis (Orchis mascula)   *scale 2/5*

Herb Robert (*Geranium robertianum*)   *scale* 2/5

Lesser Periwinkle (Vinca minor)   *scale* 1/2

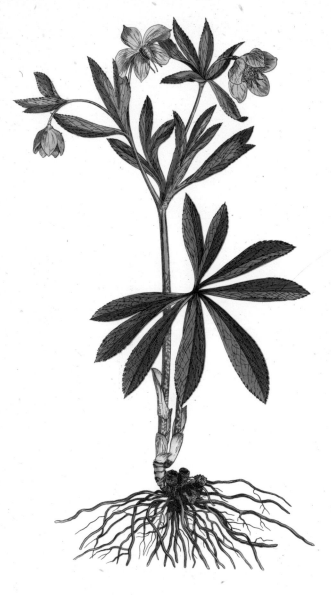

Green Hellebore (*Helleborus viridis*)   scale 2/5

Yellow Pimpernel (Lysimachia nemorum)   *scale* 1/2

Tutsan (Hypericum androsaemum)   *scale* 1/2

Deadly Nightshade (Atropa belladonna)   *scale 2/5*

Rosebay Willowherb (Epilobium angustifolium)   *scale* 1/2

Soapwort (Saponaria officinalis)   *scale 2/5*